Mat.

Mat sat.

Mat

by Bobby Lynn Maslen
pictures by John R. Maslen

Scholastic Inc.
New York • Toronto • London • Auckland • Sydney • Mexico City • New Delhi • Hong Kong • Buenos Aires

Beginning sounds for Book 1:

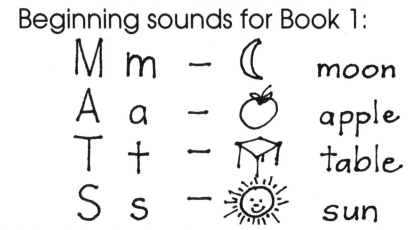

M m — moon
A a — apple
T t — table
S s — sun

Ask for Bob Books at your local bookstore, or visit www.bobbooks.com.

ISBN 0-439-17545-3

6 5 4   6 7 8 9 10 11/0

Printed in China
This edition first printing, May 2006

Sam.

Sam sat.

Mat sat. Sam sat.

Mat sat on Sam.

Sam sat on Mat.

Mat sat. Sam sat.

The End

Available Bob Books®:

Set 1: Beginning Readers
Set 2: Advancing Beginners
Set 3: Word Families
Set 4: Compound Words
Set 5: Long Vowels